Edition Schott

Piano

Nikolai Kapustin

Николай Капустин

1937 – 2020

Good Intention

(2009)

for Piano
für Klavier
для фортепиано

opus 137

Authorized Version

ED 23387
ISMN 979-0-001-21228-1

SCHOTT

www.schott-music.com

Mainz · London · Madrid · Paris · New York · Tokyo · Beijing

Good Intention

opus 137

Nikolai Kapustin
1937–2020

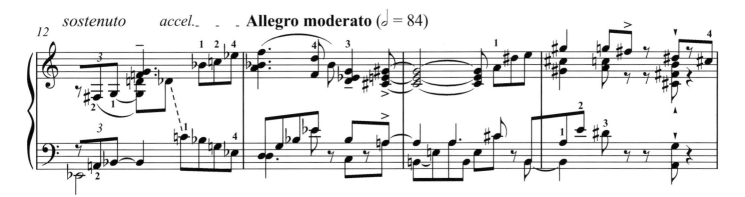

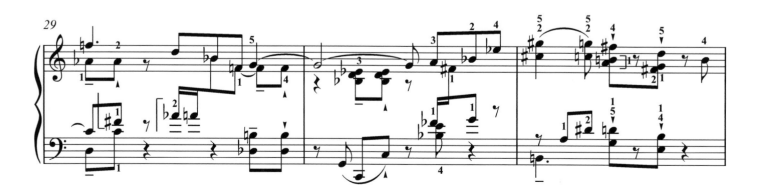

swinging

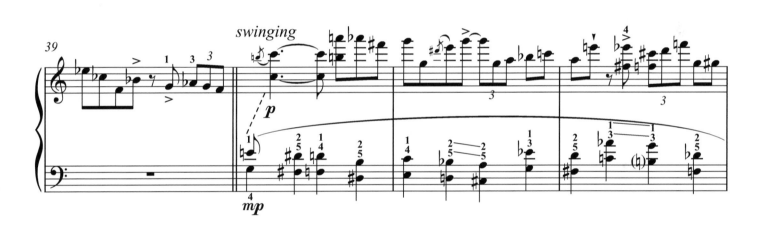

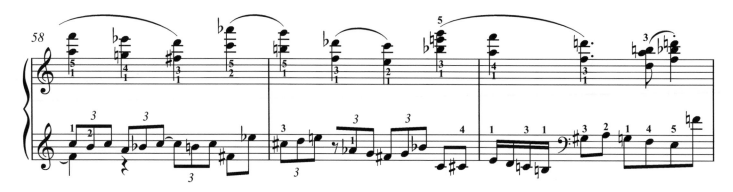

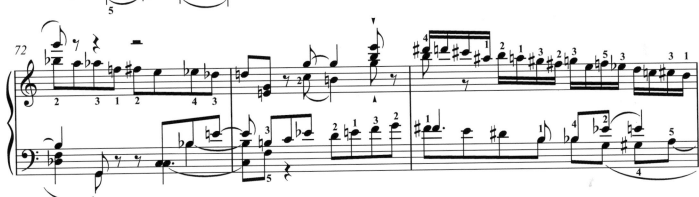

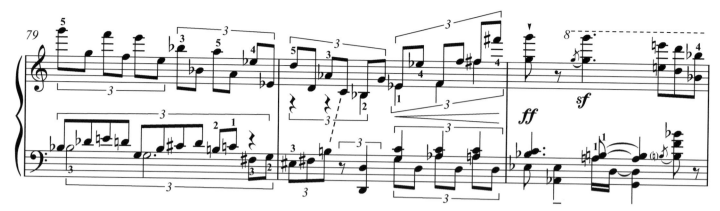

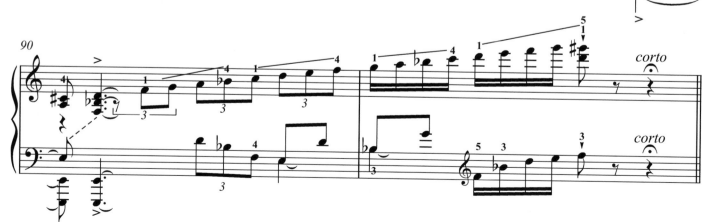

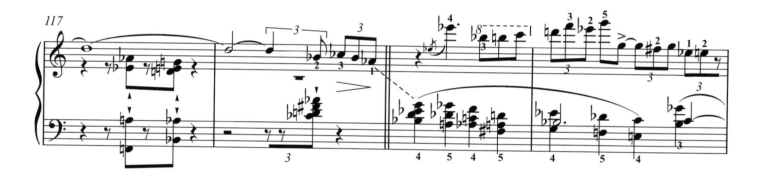

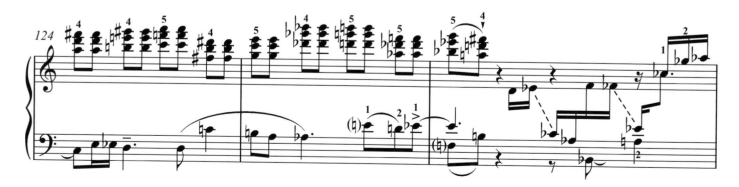

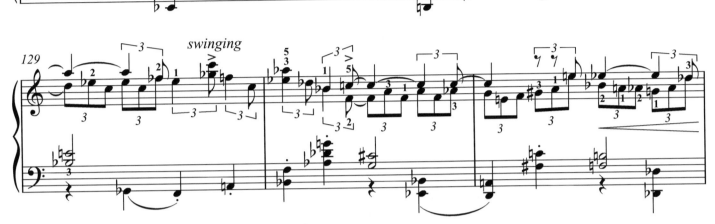

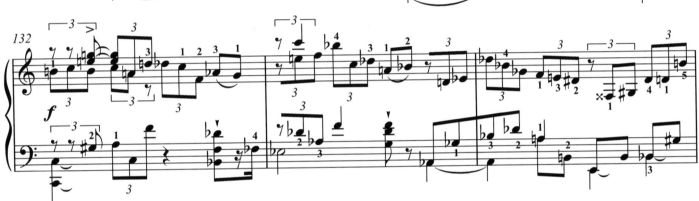

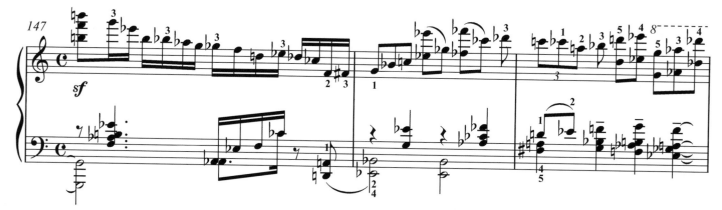

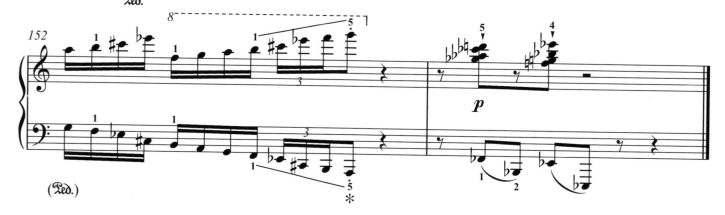

Schott Music, Mainz 59 864